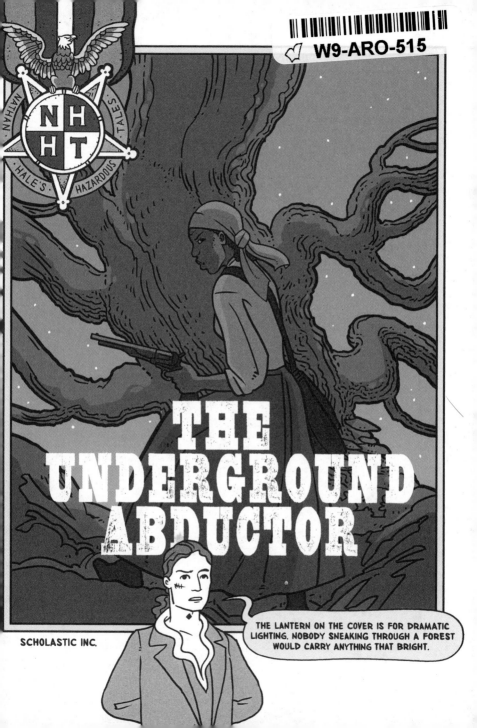

W9-ARO-515

NHHT
NATHAN HALE'S HAZARDOUS TALES

THE UNDERGROUND ABDUCTOR

SCHOLASTIC INC.

THE LANTERN ON THE COVER IS FOR DRAMATIC LIGHTING. NOBODY SNEAKING THROUGH A FOREST WOULD CARRY ANYTHING THAT BRIGHT.

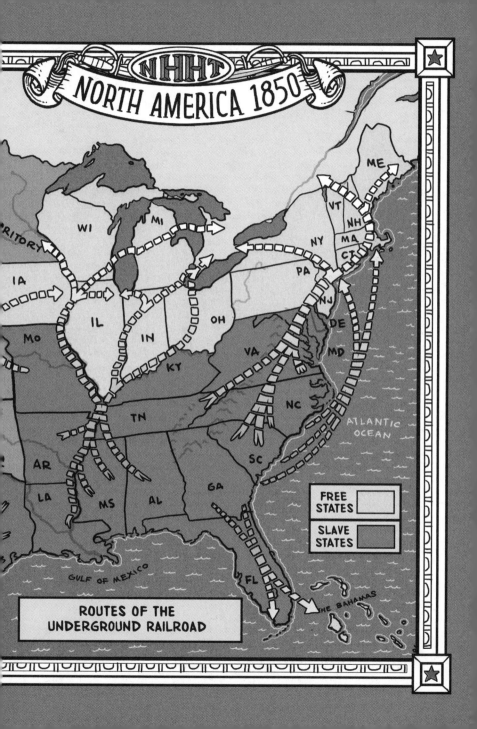

4

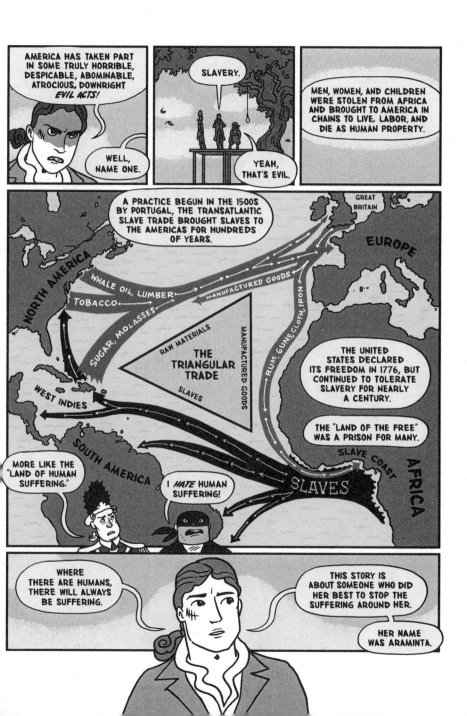

CHAPTER 1

ARAMINTA WAS A SLAVE.

AT AGE SIX, SHE ALREADY HAD A JOB AS A WEAVER'S HELPER.

NO! DO IT LIKE *THIS*!

LIKE THIS, MISSUS?

NO, NO, NO! IT'S *SIMPLE*— LIKE *THIS*!

AHHHHH...

CHOO

UGH! YOU ARE NO HELP AT *ALL*!

HOW IS SHE DOING?

WORSE THAN USELESS!

SHE'S *SLOW* AND DOESN'T DO IT RIGHT.

WE SHOULD SEND HER *BACK*!

MINTY, YOU COME HELP ME OUTSIDE.

YES, SIR.

THIS IS A MUSKRAT TRAP.

I HAVE THEM SET UP ALL OVER THIS SWAMP. I WANT YOU TO WADE IN AND CHECK THEM.

CHECK FOR MUSKRATS?

THAT'S RIGHT. IN YOU GO.

7

8

9

10

11

12

WHEN ARAMINTA ISN'T HIRED OUT, THIS IS HER HOME.

PIG IN A BAG! PIG IN A BAG!

BEN IS A PIG IN A BAG!

SWING 'IM ROUND, MINTY!

THIS IS HOW WE PLAYED WHEN BEN WAS A LI'L BABY.

SHH! YOU TWO BE QUIET AND HIDE! MR. BRODESS IS COMIN' *WITH A MAN FROM THE SOUTH!*

IS HE GONNA STEAL US AWAY?

SHHHH!

RIT AND HER CHILDREN LIVE IN CONSTANT FEAR OF BEING *SOLD.*

WHEN ARAMINTA WAS ONLY TWO, HER OLDER SISTER MARIA RITTY WAS SOLD TO A MISSISSIPPI SLAVE TRADER.

HER SISTER SOPH WAS SOLD AS WELL.

WAIT A MINUTE. IF YOU WERE A SLAVE, YOU COULD BE SOLD AWAY FROM YOUR FAMILY?

YES. HUSBANDS WERE SOLD AWAY FROM WIVES, CHILDREN FROM PARENTS, BROTHERS AND SISTERS SPLIT APART, NEVER TO BE SEEN AGAIN.

WHERE DID THEY GO?

THEY WERE SOLD SOUTH.

SLAVES WERE NOT KEPT NORTH OF MARYLAND.

HE'S GONE.

I DON'T CARE. I'M STAYIN' HID.

14

ON SUNDAYS, ARAMINTA'S FAMILY ATTENDED CHURCH.

UP COMES MOSES, AND HE SAYS TO PHARAOH, "LET MY PEOPLE GO!"

LET MY PEOPLE GO!

THAT DOESN'T LOOK LIKE A CHURCH TO ME.

MOSES DIDN'T LOOK LIKE THAT--NEITHER DID PHARAOH!

THIS IS HOW ARAMINTA SAW IT.

...AND THEN MOSES HELD OUT HIS HANDS AND COMMANDED THE SEA TO OPEN--AND IT DID! AND THE PEOPLE CROSSED ON DRY LAND.

THE STORY OF MOSES--WHO LED HIS PEOPLE OUT OF SLAVERY--WAS VERY IMPORTANT TO THE SLAVES IN AMERICA.

I CAN SEE WHY.

...WHEN EVERY LAST ONE OF THOSE CHILDREN OF ISRAEL WAS ACROSS, MOSES CLAPPED HIS HANDS TOGETHER AND THE SEA CLOSED, RIGHT ON TOP OF PHARAOH'S ARMY.

GO DOWN, MOSES, WAY DOWN TO EGYPT'S LAND,

TELL OLD PHARAOH, LET MY PEOPLE GO!

15

CHAPTER 4

NAT TURNER WAS A SLAVE IN VIRGINIA.

HE HAD VISIONS.

WHAT DO YOU MEAN, "VISIONS"?

GHOSTLY VISITATIONS!?

SORT OF.

NAT TURNER WAS DEEPLY RELIGIOUS. HE WAS A CHRISTIAN.

HIS MOTHER TAUGHT HIM THAT ONE DAY HE WOULD BECOME A *PROPHET.*

A PROPHET? LIKE MOSES OR ABRAHAM FROM THE BIBLE?

HOW SILLY!

IT WASN'T SILLY. NAT TURNER BELIEVED THE SPIRIT OF GOD SPOKE TO HIM.

IN VISIONS?

YES.

IN ONE VISION, NAT TURNER SAW HIMSELF IN A CORNFIELD.

THE LEAVES ON THE CORN WERE COVERED IN DEW.

AS HE LOOKED CLOSER, THE DEW TURNED TO BLOOD.

THEN HE WAS IN A FOREST,

WHERE THE LEAVES WERE COVERED IN HIEROGLYPHICS,

WRITTEN IN BLOOD,

AND THEY ALL SAID THE SAME THING:

"THE GREAT DAY OF JUDGMENT IS AT HAND."

This is a spooky vision.

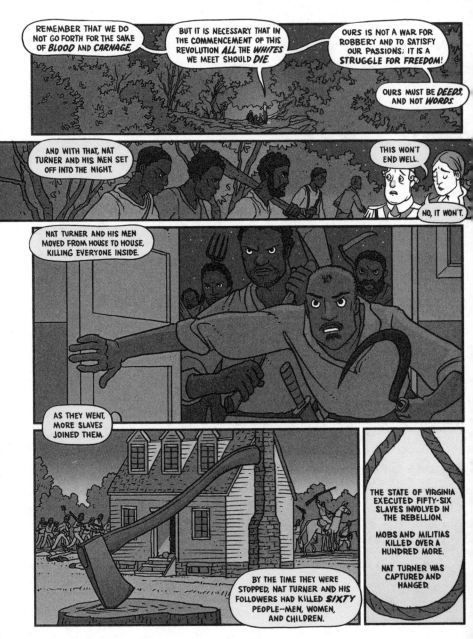

REMEMBER THAT WE DO NOT GO FORTH FOR THE SAKE OF *BLOOD* AND *CARNAGE,*

BUT IT IS NECESSARY THAT IN THE COMMENCEMENT OF THIS REVOLUTION *ALL* THE *WHITES* WE MEET SHOULD *DIE.*

OURS IS NOT A WAR FOR ROBBERY AND TO SATISFY OUR PASSIONS; IT IS A *STRUGGLE FOR FREEDOM!*

OURS MUST BE *DEEDS,* AND NOT *WORDS.*

AND WITH THAT, NAT TURNER AND HIS MEN SET OFF INTO THE NIGHT.

THIS WON'T END WELL.

NO, IT WON'T.

NAT TURNER AND HIS MEN MOVED FROM HOUSE TO HOUSE, KILLING EVERYONE INSIDE.

AS THEY WENT, MORE SLAVES JOINED THEM

THE STATE OF VIRGINIA EXECUTED FIFTY-SIX SLAVES INVOLVED IN THE REBELLION.

MOBS AND MILITIAS KILLED OVER A HUNDRED MORE.

NAT TURNER WAS CAPTURED AND HANGED.

BY THE TIME THEY WERE STOPPED, NAT TURNER AND HIS FOLLOWERS HAD KILLED *SIXTY* PEOPLE—MEN, WOMEN, AND CHILDREN.

23

MORNIN', RIT. I DON'T SEE YOUNG MINTY OUT WORKIN' TODAY.

MR. BRODESS, SHE'S *HURT*, YOU KNOW.

IF SHE'D BEEN WORKIN' INSTEAD OF WANDERIN' OFF TO THE STORE, SHE WOULDN'T HAVE *GOTTEN* HURT.

SHE NEEDS TO EARN HER KEEP!

I can work.

I'm goin' to work.

MINTY, YOU'RE *BLEEDIN'!*

I can't see anything.

MR. BRODESS HAS GOT TO LET YOU *REST*.

Can't rest, he'll sell me.

THERE'S THE ONE I MENTIONED. SHE'S A LITTLE BANGED UP, BUT SHE'S A HARD WORKER.

THE GIRL WITH THE HEAD INJURY? SHE AIN'T WORTH SIXPENCE.

MINTY!

WHUMP

I'D *TAKE* SIXPENCE.

HAH! SORRY. NO DEAL. THAT GIRL IS YOUR PROBLEM.

ARAMINTA LAY SICK IN BED FOR *MONTHS*.

HER BODY WEAKENED AND STRANGE THINGS BEGAN TO HAPPEN INSIDE HER HEAD.

WAS NAT TURNER EVER HIT IN THE HEAD? IS THAT WHY *HE* HAD VISIONS?

NO. IN FACT, THERE MAY BE NO LINK BETWEEN MINTY'S INJURY AND HER VISIONS.

THE VISIONS STARTED SOON AFTER SHE RECOVERED.

WHAT DID SHE *SEE* IN HER VISIONS?

WAIT AND SEE.

QUIT BEING SO MYSTERIOUS! WHAT DID SHE *SEE?*

ARAMINTA SPOKE OF BOTH GOOD AND BAD VISIONS.

HEAVENLY MUSIC OR TERRIBLE RIDERS WITH CHAINS -- BUT WE'LL GET TO THAT SOON ENOUGH.

AS LONG AS SHE DOESN'T HAVE VISIONS OF *BLOODY CORN.*

ARAMINTA WORKED WITH HER BROTHERS ON HER FATHER'S LUMBER CREW.

SHE GREW STRONG HAULING AND CUTTING WOOD.

LOOK AT THIS!

I'VE ALREADY CHOPPED HALF A CORD OF WOOD! BEAT THAT!

THAT'S A FINE STACK, MINTY. MY BEST *CUTTERS* CAN BARELY KEEP UP.

IT'S 'CAUSE SHE'S ALWAYS STEALIN' NAPS.

WELL, WHATEVER SHE'S DOIN', IT *WORKS.*

26

27

28

--SOUTH! MR. BRODESS WILL *NEVER* GIVE US MANUMISSION!

WHERE'D YOU GO, MINTY?

HUH? I DIDN'T GO NOWHERE. BUT I HEARD BEAUTIFUL MUSIC. DID YOU HEAR THAT?

I DIDN'T. BUT I BET IT WAS NICE.

YOU *HAVE* TO KEEP SHOWING US THOSE VISIONS.

32

CHRISTMAS DAY, DORCHESTER COUNTY JAIL

HELLO? WHO'S THERE?

BEN? IS THAT YOU?

LINAH? ARE YOU HERE TO GET ME OUT?

NO, BEN. I'M IN *CHAINS!* THEY'RE GONNA SELL ME TOO. AWAY FROM MY BABIES, BEN!

HOLD ON, SIS. WE AIN'T SOLD YET.

MY CHILDREN, MY POOR, POOR CHILDREN.

WE AIN'T SOLD YET.

DAYS LATER

WELL, BOY. OL' MR. BRODESS SEEMS TO HAVE COME INTO MONEY--

FOUR HUNDRED DOLLARS.

HE AIN'T GOIN' TO SELL YOU AFTER ALL.

LINAH?

YOU HEAR THAT, LINAH? WE AIN'T GONNA BE SOLD!

LINAH?

I SAID *YOU* WEREN'T GONNA BE SOLD.

SHE WASN'T SO LUCKY.

SHE'S GONE WITH THE CHAIN GANG.

WHERE D'YA THINK BRODESS GOT THAT FOUR HUNDRED DOLLARS?

HER CHILDREN? WHERE ARE HER CHILDREN?

THE BUYER ONLY TOOK HER. LEFT THEM KIDS BEHIND.

"RITTIA AND HER INCREASE" --*THAT MEANS HER CHILDREN*-- "UNTIL THEY ARRIVE TO FORTY-FIVE YEARS OF AGE."

HELLO?

ARE YOU UNWELL?

ARE YOU SLEEPING?

HELLO?

EXCUSE ME. YOU CAN'T SLEEP IN HERE.

TAP TAP

VISION TIME! WHAT IS SHE SEEING?

HORSES?

I DON'T GET IT.

WAIT AND SEE.

MY MOTHER SHOULD HAVE BEEN SET FREE *FIFTEEN* YEARS AGO!?

EEEP!--ER, YES. YOUR MOTHER, RITTIA, SHOULD HAVE BEEN MANUMITTED.

WHO IS THE OWNER NOW?

MR. EDWARD BRODESS!

LAW OFFICE

I'M FAMILIAR WITH MR. BRODESS. HE'S HAD A LAWSUIT AGAINST HIM BEFORE--MAYBE TWO OR THREE.

IS THAT WHAT I NEED TO FREE MY MOTHER, A LAWSUIT?

YOU DON'T HAVE ENOUGH TO PAY FOR A LAWSUIT.

WHAT CAN I DO?

SHOW MR. BRODESS THE DOCUMENT, AND HOPE HE HAS A CHANGE OF HEART.

I'VE BEEN TRYIN' TO GET HIS HEART CHANGED. HE DON'T WANNA DO IT.

WELL, IF AT FIRST YOU DON'T SUCCEED...

I'LL TRY AGAIN.

39

42

43

44

46

47

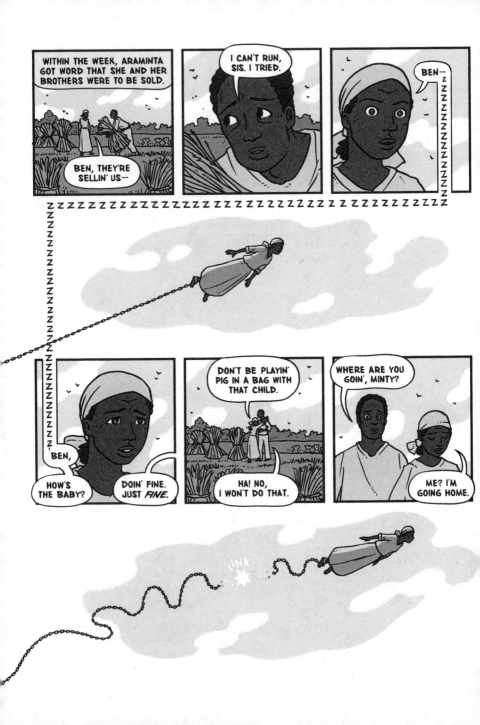

THIS IS ANOTHER *VISION*, RIGHT?

MINTY CAN'T *REALLY* FLY, CAN SHE?

IN HER VISIONS, ARAMINTA FLEW LIKE A BIRD...

...OVER HOUSES, FIELDS, AND FORESTS.

BUT THERE WAS ALWAYS ONE LAST OBSTACLE SHE COULDN'T FLY OVER.

THEN WOMEN WITH OUTSTRETCHED ARMS WOULD REACH OVER THE DIVIDE AND PULL HER ACROSS.

51

52

54

57

58

CHURCH IS THE ONLY PLACE I CAN PUT MY WORRIES AWAY AND JUST FEEL *PEACEFUL.*

BROTHERS AND SISTERS, PRESIDENT MILLARD FILLMORE HAS SIGNED A NEW BILL INTO LAW: *"THE FUGITIVE SLAVE ACT OF 1850"* —I CALL IT *"THE BLOODHOUND BILL"* BECAUSE THEY ARE GONNA USE *BLOODHOUNDS* TO TRACK EACH AND EVERY ONE OF US DOWN.

THIS NEW LAW SAYS: ANYBODY HELPIN' A SLAVE ESCAPE GETS A *ONE-THOUSAND-DOLLAR FINE* AND *SIX MONTHS IN JAIL* —AND THAT'S FOR THE *WHITE* FOLKS!

PADDY-ROLLERS CAN ARREST YOU JUST FOR *SUSPECTIN'* YOU'RE A RUNAWAY.

I KNOW, SOME DO THAT ALREADY —BUT NOW IT'S THE *LAW!* IN FACT, IF A PADDY-ROLLER *DOESN'T* ARREST YOU, HE CAN GET FINED ONE THOUSAND DOLLARS!

AND WHEN YOU GET ARRESTED, GUESS WHAT? YOU DON'T GET A *TRIAL.* YOU DON'T GET A *JURY.* YOU DON'T EVEN GET TO *DEFEND YOURSELF!*

THE BLOODHOUNDS ARE COMIN'! GONNA DRAG US ALL DOWN TO EGYPT LAND!

LORD, SAVE US FROM THE BLOODHOUND BILL!

I DON'T FEEL PEACEFUL.

HARRIET KNEW THAT IF SHE WANTED TO RESCUE HER FAMILY, SHE HAD TO ACT FAST.

59

62

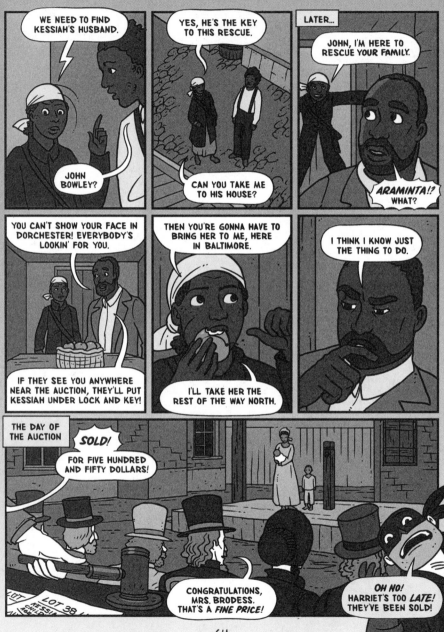

WE NEED TO FIND KESSIAH'S HUSBAND.

JOHN BOWLEY?

YES, HE'S THE KEY TO THIS RESCUE.

CAN YOU TAKE ME TO HIS HOUSE?

LATER...

JOHN, I'M HERE TO RESCUE YOUR FAMILY.

ARAMINTA!? WHAT?

YOU CAN'T SHOW YOUR FACE IN DORCHESTER! EVERYBODY'S LOOKIN' FOR YOU.

IF THEY SEE YOU ANYWHERE NEAR THE AUCTION, THEY'LL PUT KESSIAH UNDER LOCK AND KEY!

THEN YOU'RE GONNA HAVE TO BRING HER TO ME, HERE IN BALTIMORE.

I'LL TAKE HER THE REST OF THE WAY NORTH.

I THINK I KNOW JUST THE THING TO DO.

THE DAY OF THE AUCTION

SOLD! FOR FIVE HUNDRED AND FIFTY DOLLARS!

LOT 38

CONGRATULATIONS, MRS. BRODESS. THAT'S A *FINE PRICE!*

OH NO! HARRIET'S TOO *LATE!* THEY'VE BEEN SOLD!

64

65

68

HARRIET PLUNGED BACK INTO THE *MAZE* OF TOWNS, FORESTS, SWAMPS, AND RIVERS, THIS TIME WITH *NINE* PASSENGERS.

HUSH THAT BABY!

WAH! WAAH!

GIVE 'IM A FEW DROPS OF THIS.

WHAT IS IT?

ZZZZZZ

PAREGORIC.

WHAT'S PAREGORIC?

IT'S A DRUG, A TINCTURE OF OPIUM.

THEY *DRUGGED* A BABY!?

75

78

HARRIET'S BROTHERS PLANNED THEIR ESCAPE, KNOWING THAT THE COURT CASE COULD DECIDE THIER FATE AT *ANY* TIME.

WE SHOULDA JUST GONE WITH MINTY!

SPRING'S THE MOST DANGEROUS TIME TO RUN AWAY! PADDY-ROLLERS EVERYWHERE!

IT'S WHEN THE MASTERS NEED US MOST.

WE'LL TRY RUNNIN' AGAIN --*AFTER* PLANTIN' SEASON.

OR YOU COULD GO *RIGHT NOW.*

MINTY!

YOU CAME BACK FOR US!

YOU WANNA GO *NOW?!*

YUP. *THIS MINUTE.*

BUT, MINTY, IT'S *SPRING!*

RUNNIN' AWAY DURING PLANTIN', SUMMER, OR HARVEST IS A RECIPE FOR GETTIN' CAUGHT.

I DON'T BELIEVE MY EARS. MY OWN BROTHERS, *TOO CHICKEN* TO RUN--FOR THE *SECOND TIME.*

IT'S JUST A BAD TIME...

IT'S ALWAYS A *BAD TIME* WHEN YOU'RE A *SLAVE!*

YOU'D BE FREE NOW-- SET UP IN YOUR OWN HOUSE IN CANADA--IF YOU'D RUN WITH ME THE FIRST TIME!

NEXT TIME.

NEXT TIME FOR SURE.

IF *YOU* DON'T WANT FREEDOM, THERE'S PLENTY WHO *DO.*

MINTY, WAIT--

BUNCHA *SPRING CHICKENS!*

84

FORGIVE ME IF THIS SOUNDS *RUDE*--

THAT MEANS HE'S ABOUT TO SAY SOMETHING RUDE.

BUT THIS JOURNEY ALONG THE UNDERGROUND RAILROAD SEEMS, WELL... *EASY.*

HARRIET JUST MAKES IT *LOOK* EASY.

ASIDE FROM THE SLAVE HUNTERS AND PADDY-ROLLERS, THERE WERE CONSTANT DANGERS.

FUGITIVES DROWNED,

DIED OF FEVER,

FROZE TO DEATH,

LOST LIMBS TO FROSTBITE,

SUFFERED GANGRENOUS INFECTIONS, AND MORE.

SLAVES HOPPING TRAINS LOST LIMBS IF THEY JUMPED WRONG.

STOWAWAYS ON NORTHBOUND SHIPS WERE SMOKED OUT OR SUFFOCATED LIKE RATS.

SLAVES WHO WERE CAPTURED WEREN'T JUST RETURNED TO THEIR MASTER.

THEY WERE WHIPPED, BEATEN,

BRANDED--OFTEN ON THE FACE,

AND IN SOME CASES, HOBBLED.

UGRR AGENTS WHO WEREN'T AS LUCKY AS HARRIET:

ABDUCTOR CHARLES TORREY WAS CAUGHT HELPING A RUN-AWAY FAMILY IN VIRGINIA.

HE WAS SENTENCED TO FIVE YEARS OF HARD LABOR.

HE DIED AFTER TWO.

THOMAS GARRETT, THE QUAKER FROM DELAWARE, WAS BEATEN AND THROWN FROM A TRAIN WHILE TRYING TO RESCUE A SLAVE.

HE WAS THEN FINED $5,000.

ABDUCTOR CALVIN FAIRBANK WAS ARRESTED FOR AIDING SLAVES TWICE. HE SERVED SEVENTEEN YEARS IN PRISON--DURING WHICH, HE CLAIMED TO HAVE RECEIVED 35,000 LASHES.

THAT'S A LOT OF LASHES.

AND KEEP IN MIND, THESE ABDUCTORS WERE WHITE MEN, FREE, AND ABLE TO TRAVEL OPENLY ON HORSE-BACK, IN WAGONS, TRAINS, AND CARRIAGES. THEY COULD ALSO READ, WRITE, AND PROVIDE PAPERS.

HARRIET HAD NONE OF THESE ADVANTAGES. SHE WAS ILLITERATE, HAD A DEBILITATING INJURY, AND WAS HERSELF A RUNAWAY. THAT SHE TRAVELED WITHOUT CAPTURE OR LOSS IS *ASTOUNDING!*

87

91

92

94

96

97

98

100

101

102

TOO BUMPY!

TOO FAST!

TOO COLD!

I MISS MY BED!

RIT COMPLAINED THE ENTIRE TRIP.

IT JUST GOES TO SHOW: YOU CAN BE A GREAT HISTORICAL HERO,

AND YOUR MOM WILL PROBABLY STILL YELL AT YOU.

HOW CAN THEY JUST RIDE OUT IN THE OPEN LIKE THAT?

THERE COULD BE A NUMBER OF REASONS.

BEN AND RIT WERE SO OLD, THEY DIDN'T LOOK LIKE RUNAWAYS.

PLUS, THEY HAD PAPERS. TECHNICALLY, THEY WERE FREE.

HARRIET DROVE HER PARENTS NORTH. THEY BOARDED A TRAIN TO NEW YORK.

THEY HID OUT IN ROCHESTER, POSSIBLY AT FREDERICK DOUGLASS'S HOUSE.

AT LAST, THEY REACHED CANADA.

DO YOU KNOW HOW MANY GOOSES I HAD TO PLUCK TO MAKE THAT FEATHER BED?

MOMMA, THERE'S SOME PEOPLE HERE TO SEE YOU.

OH MY GOODNESS.

MOM!

MOMMA!

GRANDMA!

106

HARRIET DOESN'T STAY LONG. AFTER GETTING HER PARENTS SETTLED, SHE HEADS BACK SOUTH.

THE RACHEL RESCUE: ROUND THREE ...

RACHEL, I'VE FOUND THE KIDS, 'BOUT TWELVE MILES AWAY, ON SOME BRODESS PROPERTY.

I'LL WAIT HERE, HIDIN' OUT, TILL THE TIME IS RIGHT.

HARRIET SPENT THE SUMMER AND FALL HIDING IN DORCHESTER COUNTY.

PEOPLE SOUGHT HER OUT FOR ADVICE ON ESCAPE ROUTES.

SHE GAVE INSTRUCTIONS ON HOW TO FIND UGRR SAFE HOUSES.

DON'T TAKE THE BIG BRIDGE, IT'S GUARDED. GO UPSTREAM A FEW MILES, YOU'LL SEE A ROPE BRIDGE—zzzzzz...

MOSES?

LET HER SLEEP. SHE GOT THE CHARM.

SHE PROB'LY GETTIN' A VISION.

IT'S THE TOOTH VISION AGAIN!

TAKE THE ROPE BRIDGE --BUT ONLY AT NIGHT.

DID YOU HAVE A VISION?

I DID. A BIG WAR IS COMING.

THE CHANCE TO ABDUCT RACHEL WITH HER CHILDREN NEVER COMES.

HARRIET RETURNS TO CANADA EMPTY-HANDED.

109

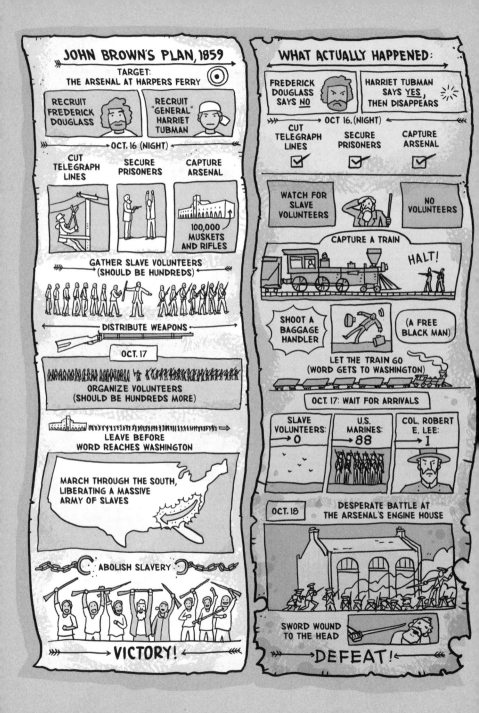

THE RACHEL RESCUE ROUND FOUR

113

114

In April 1861, Harriet's vision of a vast conflict came true.

But the book's nearly over. We don't have room for a war!

There's always room for a *WAR!*

And you thought that vision was just about a *TOOTH!*

The Civil War had begun.

Before we get to the war proper, there's one more small, strange rescue I want to talk about.

Though the war is raging, Harriet heads south to find Rachel's children.

She is unable to locate them. But she doesn't return empty-handed.

Harriet, come in. Who is this?

Who? What niece is this?

Nobody knows.

This is Margaret, my niece.

What?

There are many theories about this child. Some say that she's a lost relative, a niece who was never recorded. Some claim that she was an orphan.

There are even stranger theories claiming she was Harriet's own daughter from her short marriage to John Tubman—or even that Harriet had kidnapped her.

Huh? Which one was it?

Nobody knows. Harriet was a keeper of secrets.

Some things we just don't have answers to.

After dropping off Margaret with the abolitionist Lazette Worden, Harriet Tubman went to war.

116

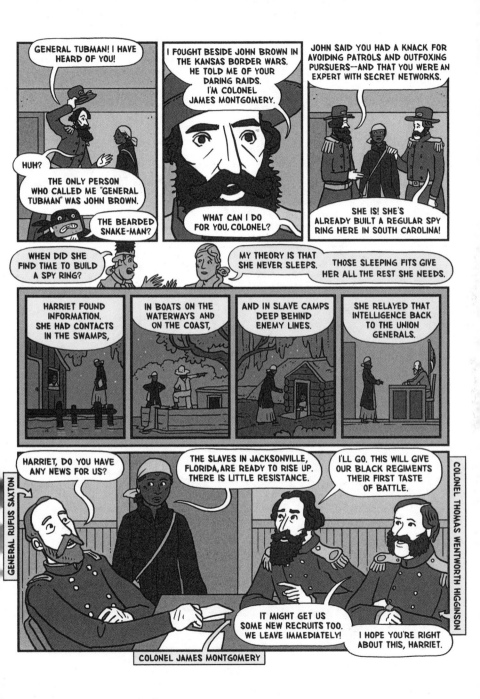

119

120

124

TO MY MOM

ISBN 978-1-338-17979-8

12 11 10 9 8 7 6 5 4 3 2   17 18 19 20 21 22

Printed in the U.S.A.   23

First Scholastic printing, January 2017

Book design by Nathan Hale and Chad W. Beckerman